Colors Glowing

A leaf is falling to the ground.
More leaves are falling all around.
They fall from branches high and low,
Spreading color as they blow.
Red and orange, they twist and twirl,
Colors glowing—all awhirl!
The grass once green from summer's sun
Is now my wondrous world of fun!
There are no leaves as nice as these,
For they are Autumn's painted leaves!

~Keith Billings

Reading 1A   Third Edition

bju press®
Greenville, South Carolina

This textbook was written by members of the faculty and staff of Bob Jones University. Standing for the "old-time religion" and the absolute authority of the Bible since 1927, Bob Jones University is the world's leading fundamental Christian university. The staff of the University is devoted to educating Christian men and women to be servants of Jesus Christ in all walks of life.

Providing unparalleled academic excellence, Bob Jones University offers over 60 undergraduate programs with dozens of concentrations and over 30 graduate programs, while its fervent spiritual emphasis prepares the minds and hearts of students for service and devotion to the Lord Jesus Christ.

If you would like more information about the spiritual and academic opportunities available at Bob Jones University, please call **1-800-BJ-AND-ME (1-800-252-6363). www.bju.edu**

NOTE:
The fact that materials produced by other publishers may be referred to in this volume does not constitute an endorsement of the content or theological position of materials produced by such publishers. Any references and ancillary materials are listed as an aid to the student or the teacher and in an attempt to maintain the accepted academic standards of the publishing industry.

READING 1A
Colors Glowing
Third Edition

Coordinating Authors	**Designers**	**Composition**
Susan J. Lehman	Holly Gilbert	Carol Larson
Linda O. Parker	David Siglin	
		Project Manager
Editor	**Cover**	Victor Ludlum
Debbie L. Parker	Elly Kalagayan	

Acknowledgments
"I Love Colors" from THEMATIC POEMS SONGS AND FINGERPLAYS by Meish Goldish. Scholastic Inc./Teaching Resources. Copyright © 1993 by Scholastic Inc. Reprinted by permission.

ISBN 978-1-59166-267-9
ISBN 978-1-59166-455-0 (READING 1A–1F Set)

15   14   13   12   11   10

Contents

Colors Glowing

The Millers

Jan Joss

illustrated by Keith Neely

It is Dad.

It is Mom.

2

It is Ashley.
It is Alex.

3

It is Buddy.

Marta Is "It"

Addy Forrest

illustrated by Keith Neely

Marta is "It."
Marta sits here.

Papá hid.
Mamá hid.

Susita hid.
Carlos hid.
"Come here, Susita!"

7

"Susita is here!"
Marta wins.

Where Did They Hide?

Circle the object that each person hid behind.

Susita

Carlos

Mamá

Papá

The Brown Hen

Gail Fitzgerald

illustrated by Keith Neely

This is Brown Hen.

10

This is Tim.

Brown Hen hit the net.

12

Brown Hen hit the tin.

14

Brown Hen is wet.
Tim is wet.

"Sit here, Brown Hen!"

16

Colors

Kathleen Hynicka
illustrated by Julie Speer

It is green.
It is a green rug.

It is red.
It is a red bug.

17

It is black.
It is a black cat.

It is blue.
It is a blue hat.

It is yellow.
It is a yellow bud.

It is brown.
It is brown mud.

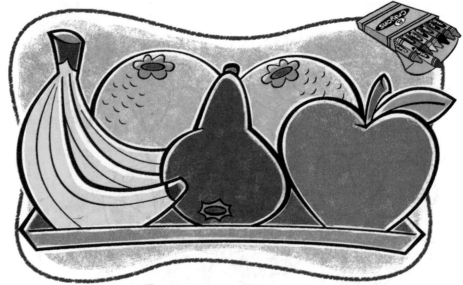

It is purple.
It is a purple fig.

It is orange.
It is an orange wig.

Colors and Rhymes

Color each object to match the color word.

green rug

red bug

blue hat

black cat

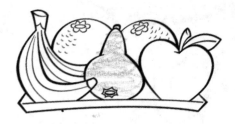

purple fig

orange wig

I Love Colors

Meish Goldfish
illustrated by John Bjerk

I love colors, yes I do!
Red and orange and green and blue!
I love colors, dark or bright,
Yellow, purple, black, and white!

Buddy

Melodye Snyder
illustrated by Keith Neely

Here is Buddy.
Buddy is a white pup.
This tub is for Buddy.

Buddy is wet.
Alex sits in the sun.

Dad is wet.
Alex is wet.

26

The pup runs.
Alex runs.
Dad runs.

The pup is brown.
Alex loves Buddy.

Pets

Elaine Johnson
illustrated by Julie Arsenault and David Schuppert

I love this pet's lick.
I love its white bib.
I love you, kit.

I love this pet's nip.
I love its black tip.
I love you, pup.

I love this pet's kick.
I love its brown neck.
I love you, kid.

I love this pet's peck.
I love its green neck.
I love you, duck.

CUBS WIN

Jan Joss

illustrated by Keith Neely

Reggie picks up his cap.
His cap is blue.
Reggie is a Cub.

Alex picks up his cap.
His cap is blue.
Alex is a Cub.

Marta sits in the sun.
Ashley sits in the sun.
Marta and Ashley are fans.
Marta and Ashley are for the Cubs.

35

Reggie is up.
His bat hits the ball.

Reggie runs!
The Cubs win!

My Team Shirt

Draw and color your own team shirt.

A Duck Picnic

Kathleen Hynicka
illustrated by Cory Godbey

Here comes a green duck.
The duck has a blue sack.
What is in the blue sack?

Here come ten brown ducks.
A duck has a red sack.
What is in the red sack?

The blue sack has nuts.
The red sack has cups.

11

The ducks sit in the sand.
The ducks sip and peck.
It is a duck picnic.

My Picnic

Color the pictures of the food that you would eat at a picnic.

Fun in the Sun

Melodye Snyder

illustrated by Paula Cheadle

The sun is up.
Nick runs in the sand.
Ted runs in the sand.

44

Nick has a blue cup.
Ted has a yellow tub.
They get wet sand.

Nick tips the blue cup.
Ted tips the yellow tub.
Nick pats the sand.

The sun hid.
Nick ran in the sand.
Ted ran in the sand.

Up the Hill

Hilda Ritter
illustrated by Keith Neely

The Big Hill

"Come," said Papá.
"Let's get up this hill."

"I can get up the hill," said Carlos.
"I can get up the hill," said Marta.

Mamá will get up the hill.
Papá will get up the hill.
Marta will get up the hill.

Did Carlos get up the hill?
Carlos fell.

Fun Up Here

Papá went back to Carlos.
"I fell," said Carlos.

"Can you get up?" said Papá.
"I can get up," said Carlos.
"I will sit here for a bit.
But I can get up the hill."

Marta is up the hill.
Here come Mamá and Susita.

Papá is here.
Carlos is here.
"Come sit here," said Papá.
"Mamá has a snack for us."
"It is fun up here," said Marta.

Mother Hen

Melodye Snyder
illustrated by Julie Arsenault

Mother Hen!
What will you do?
I will peck in the brown sand.
Cluck! Cluck!

Mother Hen!
What will you do?
I will nip at a black bug.
Cluck! Cluck!

Mother Hen!
What will you do?
I will sit on a white egg.
Cluck! Cluck!

Mother Hen!
What will you do?
I will tend to a yellow chick.
Cluck! Cluck!

Mother Hen, what did you do?

60

Lots of Dots

Milly Howard and Ann Larson
illustrated by Anne Bastine and David Schuppert

Here are green dots.
Green dots are in a pod.
What are the green dots?

Here are lots of brown dots.
Brown dots are in a pig.
What are the brown dots?

Here are lots and lots of black dots.
Black dots are on Spot.
What are the black dots?

Underwater Dots

Follow the alphabet to connect the dots.

Color the picture.

BRILLIANT

A
B C
D E F
G
Z
Y
X H
W
V I
J
U T S R K L M
Q N
P O

An Elk Hunt

Jan Joss
illustrated by Cory Godbey

Mr. Kent had a gun.
Mr. Hill had a bag.
They set off to hunt an elk.

"I am wet," said Mr. Kent.
"It is the sun," said Mr. Hill.
"The sun is hot."

The men sat a bit.
They did not see the elk.

The elk got the bag.
The elk got the gun.
The men did not get the elk.

Stop
and
Go

Gail Fitzgerald
illustrated by Lynda Slattery

Stop

The light is green.
The orange cab must stop.
The yellow bus must stop.
The big red truck must stop.

69

The men will stop.
They are not upset.
They want to help.

Here comes a big dog.
Here come a lot of pups.
1, 2, 3, 4, 5, 6, 7, 8, 9, 10.
Mother has ten pups!

71

Go

One pup stops to rest.
The man picks it up.

72

"You must not stop here."
1, 2, 3, 4, 5, 6, 7, 8, 9, 10.
Ten pups go fast.

73

The orange cab can go.
The yellow bus can go.
The big red truck can go.

Stop and Go

Color in each traffic light and complete the sentence.

| stop   go |

Green says to _go_.

Red says to _stop_.

To the Vet

Milly Howard and Jan Joss
illustrated by Tim Davis

Kim Is Sick

"Kim is sick," I said.
Father got in the van.
Kim and I got in the van.
Kim went to the vet.

76

Kim it at the big dog.
The big dog bit at Kim.
Kim ran

Kim sat on Father's lap.
A man had a big dog.
A mother had a white pup.

Kim hit at the big dog.
The big dog bit at Kim.
Kim ran.

The big dog went to get Kim.
The white pup went to get Kim.
"This is bad," I said.

Get the Pets

I got up to stop Kim.
But I hit the desk.

The man got up to stop his dog.
But his leg hit a stand.
The mother got up to stop the pup.
But the mother's hand hit the bell.

"Get your pets!" said the vet.
The man got his big dog.
The mother got the white pup.

I got Kim at last.
"Sit still, Kim!" I said.
And Kim did.

My Pet

Draw and color a picture of the pet that you would like to find at the pet store.

Circle any item below that your pet might need.

Joseph's Coat

from Genesis 37 retold by Milly Howard
illustrated by Preston Gravely

Now Israel loved Joseph more than all his children, because he was the son of his old age: and he made him a coat of many colours.
–Genesis 37:3

Come, Joseph

Joseph sat on a hill.
Joseph rested in the sun.
The sun lit the colors in his coat.

"Come, Joseph," said a man.
"Your father sent for you."

Joseph went to his father.
"Here is a gift," his father said.
"It is for your brothers.
They are west of here."
Joseph ran west.

The Brothers

"Here comes Joseph," said one brother.
"Father has jobs for us!
But Father gives him gifts."

Joseph ran to the camp.
Joseph handed the gift to his brothers.
They did not want the gift.
The brothers wanted to kill Joseph.
"Come, let's get his coat!"

"Let's dump Joseph in this pit."
The brothers got his coat.

One brother wanted to help Joseph.
But the brothers sent Joseph to Egypt.

The Lord took care of Joseph, and he later became a leader in Egypt. When a great famine came to their region, his brothers traveled to Egypt to get grain. God gave Joseph a forgiving spirit, and he helped to provide food for his brothers.

Joseph's brothers said, "Help us!"
Joseph wanted to give help.
God let him help his brothers.

Max the Mixer

Milly Howard
illustrated by Dana Thompson

Max will mix blue and yellow.
What color will Max have?

Max will mix red and yellow.
What color will Max have?

Max will mix blue and red.
What color will Max have?

Max will mix six colors.
What color will Max have?

Max has a mess!
But you must not fuss!

Russ will fix the mixer.
And Russ will get up the mess.

Here Comes the Parade

Jan Joss and Milly Howard
illustrated by Keith Neely

The Parade

"The parade will pass here," Dad said.

"You and Mother and I can sit here."

"Will Reggie come here?" I said.

"Yes, Janna. Reggie will come here," Mom said.

"Here comes the parade!" Mom said.
Ten men went step, step.
The parade was fun.
"But Reggie is not here yet," I said.
"Reggie will miss the parade."

A man had six oranges.
Up, up went the oranges.
And not one orange fell!
The parade was fun.
"But Reggie is not here," I said.
"Reggie will miss the parade."

Reggie

A big band went step, step.
Many men had on red vests.
They did not miss any steps.
The parade was fun.
"But Reggie is not here yet," I said.
"Reggie will miss the parade."

99

"Quick, get up," said Mom.
"Janna, the flags are here!"
Mom and Dad and I got up.

"Here is Reggie," I said.
Reggie had one of the flags.
Alex had one of the flags.
"Reggie did not miss the parade," I said.
"Reggie is in the parade!"

Here Comes Reggie

Draw and color the item Reggie carried in the parade.